GREAT MINDS® WIT & WISDOM

Grade 7 Module 2:
Americans All

Student Edition

COPYRIGHT STATEMENT

Student Edition

GRADE 7, MODULE 2

Lesson Handouts

Handout 1A: "Benjamin O. Davis, Jr."

Handout 2A: *Sacred* and the Morpheme *Sacr*

Handout 3A: Character Analysis

Handout 3B: Fluency Homework

Handout 4A: ToSEEC Paragraph Model

Handout 4B: Informative Essay Structure

Handout 6A: Plot and Character Analysis

Handout 7A: Speaking and Listening Goal-Setting and Self-Assessment

Handout 7B: Socratic Seminar Discussion Starters

Handout 7C: Word Relationships

Handout 8A: Chapter 6 Ideas and Events

Handout 8B: *Code Talker* World War II Map

Handout 8C: "Pearl Harbor and World War II"

Handout 8D: Fluency Homework

Handout 8E: Content Vocabulary and the Suffix *–ism*

Handout 9A: Headlines

Handout 9B: Ned Begay, Navajo and Marine

Handout 9C: Frayer Model

Handout 10A: Examining Style

Handout 11A: Central Ideas: Chapter 10

Handout 11B: Examining Transitions

Handout 12A: Boarding School/Code School Comparison

Handout 12B: Fluency Homework

Handout 12C: Transitional Phrases and Clauses Guide

Handout 12D: Transition Experimentation

Handout 13A: Outside-In

Handout 14A: Word Exploration

Handout 14B: Examining Style and Tone

Handout 14C: Tone Words

Handout 16A: Fluency Homework

Handout 17A: Content, Style, and Structure

Handout 18A: "Navajo Code Talkers"

Handout 18B: Informational Text Analysis

Handout 19A: Before, During, and After Chart

Handout 19B: Speaking and Listening Goal-Setting and Self-Assessment

Handout 20A: ToSEEC Paragraph Organizer

Handout 21A: Checklist for Focusing Question Task 2

Handout 21B: ToSEEC Paragraph Structure Review

Handout 23A: "Relocation Camps"

Handout 24A: Transition Revision

Handout 25A: Tableau Planning Sheet

Handout 27A: Photography Analysis

Handout 27B: Fluency Homework

Handout 29A: Content Vocabulary Word Relationships

Handout 30A: Speaking and Listening Goal-Setting and Self-Assessment

Handout 30B: Central Idea Analysis

Handout 30C: Using Modifying Phrases and Clauses

Handout 32A: Informative Essay Model

Handout 33A: EOM Task Planner

Handout 35A: Informative Essay Checklist

Handout 35B: Editing and Revising for Style and Conventions

Volume of Reading Reflection Questions

Wit & Wisdom Parent Tip Sheet

Name _____

Date _____ Class _____

Handout 1A: "Benjamin O. Davis, Jr."

Directions: Read this article to learn more about an individual who fought during World War II and about the concepts of *equality* and *marginalization*.

Benjamin O. Davis, Jr.
'Determined to Succeed' by Alexis O'Neill

1. When Benjamin O. Davis, Jr., took his first ride in an airplane as a teenager in 1926, his life was changed forever. "I was completely overwhelmed," he said. "We flew in an open-cockpit airplane… About all I remember are the takeoff and the feeling of exhilaration at being in the air… and I remember a sudden surge of determination to become an aviator."

2. The way to make this dream come true was through the military. Davis's father, who had risen from enlisted man to officer in the U.S. Army, urged him to apply to the U.S. Military Academy at West Point. There he would receive a high-quality education and enter the military as an officer. Davis's father believed that African Americans had an important role to play in the military and thought that his son could be instrumental in making changes there.

3. Young Davis failed the entrance exam to West Point the first time he took it. But he was "determined to succeed." He passed it on his second try in 1932.

4. Davis was the only black cadet at West Point. In those days, official military instructions claimed that blacks were inferior to whites and lacked courage and strong moral character. Upperclassmen at West Point wanted Davis to quit, so they enforced a "silencing" against him. For four years, no one talked to Davis. "Throughout my career at West Point and beyond, it was often difficult to reconcile the principles of Duty, Honor, and Country with the Army's inhuman and unjust treatment of individuals on the basis of race," Davis later said. His ability to endure the silencing made him strong. He never complained to his family, classmates, or superiors.

5. Davis's graduation in 1936 made headlines. He was the first African American to graduate from West Point in the twentieth century. But when he applied to fly in the Army Air Corps, he was rejected. No African American units were to be included in the Air Corps because whites were unwilling to have African American commanders.

6   In 1941, the War Department approved the formation of an all-African American flying unit. After flight training at Tuskegee Institute in Alabama, Davis was placed in command of the 99th Pursuit Squadron. By 1943, he was leading his men in missions against enemy forces in North Africa and the Mediterranean. For his leadership during a bomber escort mission, Davis received the Distinguished Flying Cross.

7   When the war in Europe ended in May 1945, Davis expected to lead missions against Japan. Instead, he returned to the United States to lead the all-African American 477th Bombardment Group. Before the unit was sent into action, the war in the Pacific ended.

8   Unfortunately, another kind of war was continuing in the United States: segregation and the fight to change it. Substandard living quarters, schooling, and treatment of African American veterans appalled Davis. In 1946, the 332nd and the 477th moved to Lockbourne Air Base in Columbus, Ohio. For the first time ever, African Americans administered an Army Air Force base in the United States without the immediate supervision of white officers. "Lockbourne became one of the best bases in the Air Force," Davis said. He continued his distinguished military career until his retirement in 1970, when he turned his talents to public service.

9   Although Davis is proud of having graduated from West Point, he wrote in his autobiography, "I do not find it complimentary to me or to the nation to be called 'the first black West Point graduate in this century.' We are all simply Americans[;] ... surely the unnecessary labeling of people by race, religion, or ethnicity does nothing to bring the many diverse groups of American society together."

10   Benjamin O. Davis, Jr., demonstrated his determination to succeed, his skill as a pilot, his courage in battle, and his patriotism in spite of many obstacles. And he was able to make things better for those who came after him.

Citation: O'Neill, Alexis. "Benjamin O. Davis, Jr.: 'Determined to Succeed.'" Cobblestone. Cobblestone Publishing Co. 1997

Name _____

Date _____ Class _____

Handout 2A: *Sacred* and the Morpheme *Sacr*

Directions: In Part I, predict the part of speech and meaning of *sacred*, and write a sentence using the word. In Part II, answer the questions about the root *sacr* and words with related meanings. Finally, in Part III, reflect on the significance of believing that the land is sacred.

I. Examples of *Sacred* Used in Context

"When we Indians fought on those far-off islands, we always kept the thought in our minds that we were defending Our Mother, the <u>sacred</u> land that sustained us" (Bruchac 2).

The Navajos considered land to be <u>sacred</u> and accordingly treated it with the utmost respect and care.

sacred

Part of Speech:

Definition:

_____

_____

Example Sentence Using *Sacred*:

_____

_____

_____

II. The Root *Sacr*

sacrifice the surrender of something valuable (n.); to give up out of devotion (v.)

"He offered a <u>sacrifice</u> to the gods."

sacrilege the destruction of a place or thing thought to be holy (n.)

"She thought it was <u>sacrilege</u> to speak badly of the dead."

From the word *sacred*, and the words *sacrifice* and *sacrilege*, what can you determine that the root *sacr* means?

_____

_____

What are some other words with meanings that are related but that have different roots?

_____

_____

III.   The Sacred Land

In *Code Talker*, the protagonist says that he believed that he had to fight for his country because "we were defending Our Mother, the <u>sacred</u> land that sustains us" (2). If a person believes that the land is sacred, what might he or she do differently from someone who does not believe that the land is sacred?

_____

_____

_____

_____

Name Gannon Reins

Date _____ Class _____

Handout 3A: Character Analysis

Directions: Based on the text, choose a word or phrase that describes a trait that Kii Yázhí possesses, and write that in the first column. In the second column, support your choice with evidence from the text, including page references. In the third column, elaborate on the evidence by explaining how it supports the word or phrase you identified in the first column. Continue as time permits.

Trait	Evidence	Elaboration
Loyal	- Ki Yohzi is loyal because he is ok with people punishing him over Navojo language.	- Ki Yohzi is beaten and is still loyal to his teachers.
Dedicated	- Ki Yohzi goes through many thing but still goes to school for his family.	- He is doing this all for his family.
Respectful	- Ki Yohzi is Respectful because he gave the teacher a nice greeting in Navojo language.	- Ki Yozhi was being nice in Navajo but the teacher did not care, he did not like Navajo

Name _____

Date _____   Class _____

Handout 3B: Fluency Homework

Directions:

1. Day 1: Read the text carefully, and annotate to help you read fluently.
2. Each day:
   a. Practice reading the text aloud three to five times.
   b. Evaluate your progress by placing a checkmark in the appropriate unshaded box.
   c. Ask someone (adult or peer) to listen and evaluate you as well.
3. Last day: Respond to the self-reflection questions at the end of this handout.

"You are small," my grandfather said, as if he could hear what I was thinking. "But your heart is large. You will do your best."

I nodded.

When I stepped outside, my mother bent down and embraced me much harder than my grandfather had hugged me. Then she stepped back to stand by the door of our hogan.

"Travel safely, my son," Mother said. Her voice was so sad.

My father came up to me and put his broad, calloused hands on my shoulders. He, too, was wearing his best clothing and jewelry. Though he said nothing, I think Father was even sadder than my mother, so sad that words failed him. He was shorter than her, but he was very strong and always stood so straight that he seemed tall as a lodgepole pine to me. His eyes were moist as he lifted me up to the wagon seat and then nodded.

(Bruchac 6–7)

Student Performance Checklist:	Day 1		Day 2		Day 3		Day 4	
	You	Listener*	You	Listener	You	Listener*	You	Listener*
Accurately read the passage three to five times.								
Read with appropriate phrasing and pausing.								
Read with appropriate expression.								
Read articulately at a good pace, and an audible volume.								

*Adult or peer

Self-reflection: What choices did you make when deciding how to read this passage, and why? What would you like to improve on or try differently next time?

Name

Date   Class

Handout 4A: ToSEEC Paragraph Model

Directions: When directed in class, read and annotate the paragraph to indicate how each sentence fits within the ToSEEC paragraph structure. Use Handout 4B as a reference as needed.

The recovery of the Navajo nation that took place over the century and a half after the 1860s is remarkable in light of the devastation they endured during the Long Walk and their exile from their homeland. Today the Navajo nation comprises 26,897 square miles. It is the largest Indian reservation in the United States. There are more than 200,000 Navajos. Although it is not without its problems and challenges, the Navajo nation has been described as one of the most economically prosperous and forward-looking of all the American Indian nations in the United States. The nation is large and successful despite facing adversity that could have utterly destroyed it. Their ability to rebound so dramatically from their historic marginalization shows the incredible strength and resilience of the Navajo people.

Note: This paragraph is a modified version of one contained in the Author's Note to *Code Talker*, pages 217–218.

Name _____

Date _____ Class _____

Handout 4B: Informative Essay Structure

Directions: Refer to the following model for guidance in structuring an informative writing piece.

Introductory Paragraph

H	Hook	Catch your audience's attention.	
I	Introduce	Introduce your audience to the topic.	
T	Thesis	State your essential idea about the topic,	
		and preview your	supporting points.

Body Paragraph

To S	Topic Statement	State a point that supports your thesis.	
EC	Evidence	Cite evidence for your point, including necessary context.	
E	Elaboration	Explain how the evidence relates to the point.	
C	Concluding Statement	Close the paragraph.	

	Topic Statement	Transition from your last point, and	state another point that supports your thesis.
	Evidence	Cite evidence for your point, including necessary context.	
	Elaboration	Explain how the evidence relates to the point.	
	Concluding Statement	Close the paragraph.	

Conclusion

C	Conclusion	Reinforce your thesis, reflecting on its significance.

Name _____

Date _____ Class _____

Handout 6A: Plot and Character Analysis

Directions: The first column lists actions of the officials at the boarding school. In the second column, briefly describe the resulting effects on Ned or other students. In the third column, describe how some of the traits of Ned Begay either help him deal with what happens or make it harder for him to do so.

What Boarding School Officials or Teachers Do	Effect on Ned Begay or Other Students	Traits That Impact Ned Begay
Ban students from speaking Navajo and punish them if they do.	— Ned Begay and the others in his class wooa bonn ed	
Greet the students with anger and yelling.		
Take the students' Navajo clothing and jewelry and replace it with drab uniforms.		

What Boarding School Officials or Teachers Do	Effect on Ned Begay or Other Students	Traits That Impact Ned Begay
Cut the students' hair.		
Change the students' names.		

Name _____

Date _____ Class _____

Handout 7A: Speaking and Listening Goal-Setting and Self-Assessment

Directions: Use this tool to set a goal for and assess your participation in the Socratic Seminar.

Before the Discussion: Set a Goal

My goal for this discussion is to:

After the Discussion: Self-Assess

Criteria	+/ Δ *
I came prepared for the discussion.	
I posed questions.	
I responded to questions.	
I made relevant observations.	
I acknowledged and built on others' ideas.	
I listened carefully.	
I brought the discussion back on topic as needed.	
I agreed and disagreed respectfully.	
▪ I did not interrupt.	
▪ I used a polite tone of voice.	
▪ I disagreed with the statement, not the person.	
I used appropriate, formal, academic language. For example:	
I used vocabulary that I learned in this module, such as these words:	

* (+ = *Good performance* Δ = *Needs improvement*)

I met my goal for this discussion.   YES   /   NO

Explain:

My goal for the next discussion is to:

_____

_____

_____

_____

Name _____

Date _____ Class _____

Handout 7B: Socratic Seminar Discussion Starters

Directions: During our Socratic Seminar or classroom discussions, you will want to speak clearly, support your ideas thoughtfully, listen to your classmates, and use academic English.

The sentence frames below will help with all of these goals for academic discussion. Challenge yourself to use them in our classroom discussions.

When You Want to State Your Opinion or Share an Idea:

1 I believe that_____because_____.

2 I think that_____because_____.

3 When the author wrote_____, this made me think that_____.

4 According to the author,_____. So, it seems obvious that_____.

5 I think an important idea is that_____.

6 Because of_____, we can tell that_____.

When You Want to Ask for More Information or Clarity:

1 Can you explain what you mean by_____?

2 I am confused about_____. Do you mean that_____?

3 In other words, are you saying that_____?

4 Can you say more about that?

5 Where do you see that in the book?

6 Can you give an example of_____?

When You Want to Change the Subject:

1 Does anyone have anything else to add about_____?

2 If no one has more to say about_____, I'd like to move on to talk about_____.

When You Want to Agree and Add More to an Idea:

1 I really like_____'s idea about_____.

2 I agree. In addition,_____.

3 I'd like to go back to what_____said about_____.

When You Want to Disagree and Present a Different Idea:

1 I see what_____means, but I think that_____.

2 I can see your point, but from my perspective,_____.

3 I partly agree, but I also think that_____.

Name

Date

Class

Handout 7C: Word Relationships

Directions: Fill in the table to think about the words *culture* and *tradition*.

culture	Word Relationships	tradition
Definition:	Relationship:	Definition:
Synonyms or Related Words:	Related Words:	Synonyms or Related Words:
Sentence with the Word *culture*:	New Sentence with Both Words:	Sentence with the Word *tradition*:

Name

Date   Class

Handout 8A: Chapter 6 Ideas and Events

Directions: Chapter 6 of *Code Talker* is organized in three parts: background description about Japan at the start of World War II, an overview of the Navajo perspective at the start of World War II, and details about the events of Sunday, December 7, 1941, both for the protagonist of the novel and for the nation as a whole.

For each of these three parts, note two important ideas or events the author develops.

Part 1: Japan at the Start of World War II	Part 2: The Navajos at the Start of World War II	Part 3: Details about Sunday, December 7, 1941
Idea #1:	Idea #1:	The Protagonist's Experience on That Day:
Idea #2:	Idea #2:	The National Event on That Day:

Name

Date   Class

Handout 8B: *Code Talker* World War II Map

Directions: Use this map to locate some of the places described or referenced in *Code Talker*.

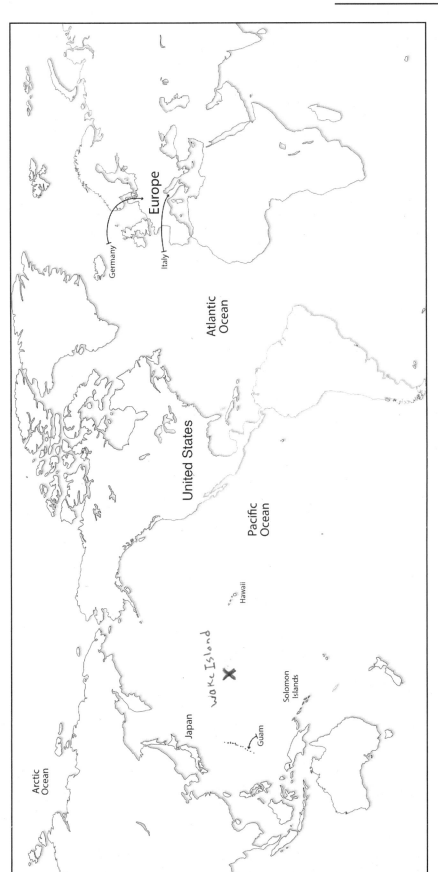

Note: Care was taken in the creation of this map. Great Minds®, however, cannot guarantee the positional accuracy of the locations depicted on this map.

Name _____

Date _____   Class _____

Handout 8C: "Pearl Harbor and World War II"

Directions: Read this article to learn more about World War II.

Pearl Harbor and World War II
by Brandon Marie Miller and Mark Clemens

1   While trouble was brewing in the rest of the world, America had its own problems in the 1930s—it was stuck in a severe economic depression. Americans did not want to get involved in another "European mess," as they had during World War I (1914–1918). As President Franklin D. Roosevelt said, "We seek to isolate ourselves from war." But U.S. isolationism, a policy of not getting involved in the political or economic situations of other countries, came at a dangerous time. Building on the bitterness and bad conditions that resulted from Germany's loss in World War I, Adolf Hitler was rising to power in that country. By the mid-1930s, using violence and hatred to spread his fascist ideas, Hitler and the Nazi party had gained control of Germany.

2   Other aggressive nations also were on the rise. Italian dictator Benito Mussolini looked to extend his empire into North Africa. He invaded Ethiopia in 1935. In 1936, Mussolini joined forces with Hitler in the Rome–Berlin Axis. Japan also had dreams of becoming an imperial force.

3   Meanwhile, Hitler began re-arming Germany. In March 1938, he took over Austria. When Hitler threatened to swallow up part of Czechoslovakia, the other European powers did not stand in his way in the hope of preventing a war.

4   But Hitler would not stop. He invaded the rest of Czechoslovakia, and then, on September 1, 1939, he attacked Poland. Two days later, France and Great Britain declared war on Germany and Italy.

5   By mid-June 1940, a shocked America watched as France surrendered to the Nazis. Germany then focused its firepower on Great Britain, raining bombs on England in July 1940 in what became known as the Battle of Britain. British prime minister Winston Churchill flooded Roosevelt with pleas for help.

6   Roosevelt knew that the United States needed to aid England. In the spring of 1941, American supplies began pouring into England, and a few months later, into the Soviet Union after Hitler invaded it in June 1941. The United States was the "arsenal of democracy."

7   Japan, meanwhile, had joined forces with Germany and Italy in September 1940. After invading China, Japanese troops were pushing into Southeast Asia.

8   The United States hoped to stop Japan by restricting the sale of oil and steel to that country. In July 1941, all Japanese assets in America were frozen. But Japan pushed onward.

9   Early on a Sunday morning in December, hundreds of Japanese planes came screaming out of the sky over the Hawaiian island of Oahu. They dropped bombs and torpedoes and covered the ground with machine gun fire. Their target: the U.S. naval base at Pearl Harbor. Two hours later, more than 2,400 Americans were dead and 18 ships and 188 airplanes had been destroyed.

10 The attack came as a complete surprise to the American people. December 7, 1941, was "a date which will live in infamy," President Franklin D. Roosevelt declared. He told the American people "that since the unprovoked attack by Japan. . .a state of war has existed between the United States and the Japanese empire." Three days later, Germany and Italy declared war on the United States.

11 Over the next four years, the United States changed from a nation trying to isolate itself from the world's problems to becoming a leader among nations. It raised and supplied a huge fighting force. Americans produced guns, vehicles, vessels, aircraft, and manpower. Hundreds of thousands of American soldiers enlisted to fight overseas. Meanwhile, the men and women who remained at home did not remain untouched by the war. They filled the jobs left empty by the men who became soldiers. World War II was an event that impacted the world, and the lives of all Americans were altered by it.

Citation: Miller, Brandon Marie; Mark Clemens. "Pearl Harbor and World War II: The Year Is 1941." Cobblestone. Cobblestone Publishing Co. 2010.

Name _____

Date _____ Class _____

Handout 8D: Fluency Homework

Directions:

1. Day 1: Read the text carefully, and annotate to help you read fluently.
2. Each day:
   a. Practice reading the text aloud three to five times.
   b. Evaluate your progress by placing a checkmark in the appropriate unshaded box.
   c. Ask someone (adult or peer) to listen and evaluate you as well.
3. Last day: Respond to the self-reflection questions at the end of this handout.

Bright late autumn sun was shining through the windows of our dormitory, but there was no sun in my heart. In the other corner of the room several of my friends were laughing and talking, but I was in no mood for anything but silence. I was still smarting from what had happened to me two days before. I was so embarrassed. Although, as I have explained, I tried to be careful when I spoke our sacred language, that Friday I had been caught. Mr. Straight overheard me greeting one of my friends in Navajo when I thought no teachers were around. It didn't matter that I could now speak English as well as any *bilagáanaa*. It didn't matter how good my grades had been in all my classes. By speaking one word in our sacred language I had just proved to my teacher that I was as hopeless as the rest of my people.

(Bruchac 37)

Student Performance Checklist:	Day 1		Day 2		Day 3		Day 4	
	You	Listener*	You	Listener	You	Listener*	You	Listener*
Accurately read the passage three to five times.								
Read with appropriate phrasing and pausing.								
Read with appropriate expression.								
Read articulately at a good pace, and an audible volume.								

*Adult or peer

Self-reflection: What choices did you make when deciding how to read this passage, and why? What would you like to improve on or try differently next time?

Name _____

Date _____ Class _____

Handout 8E: Content Vocabulary and the Suffix –ism

Directions: For Part I, add examples of words that demonstrate each meaning. For Part II, write a sentence as directed, using the –ism words provided.

Part I

Word Part	Meaning	Examples
–ism (suffix)	1. The act, practice, or process of doing something.	
	2. Unfair treatment of a group of people with a specific quality.	
	3. Following certain principles, theories, or a system of thought.	

Part II

1 Use the word *isolationism* in a sentence, describing the United States before World War II.
[See the article "Pearl Harbor and World War II" (Handout 8C) if you need ideas to get started.]

_____

_____

_____

2 Use the word *patriotism* to describe the Navajos at the start of World War II. (Look back through *Code Talker* if you need ideas to get you started.)

_____

_____

_____

Name

Date   Class

Handout 9A: Headlines

Directions: Look at the real-life Pearl Harbor newspaper headlines, and then review the tips for effective headlines and the example from chapter 6 of *Code Talker*. Then, write your own headline, as directed by your teacher. Your chapter headline should:

- Follow the "Tips for Effective Headlines."
- Emphasize the most important event or events from the chapter.
- Include a headline (in all CAPITAL letters) and a subhead (In Title Case).

Real-Life Pearl Harbor Newspaper Headlines

Tips for Effective Headlines

- Use specific details (like numbers).
- Make it urgent and important.
- Use few words—and no difficult vocabulary.
- Use all capitals for the header; title case for the subhead.
- Start with a noun, not a verb.
- Use precise nouns and strong action verbs.
- Go ahead and skip articles (like *and*, *the*, *a*, or *an*).
- Chapter 7: "Navajos Wanted"

Heading!: JAPAN BoMBS PEARl HARBOR

Sub Heading: Seargent Frank Shinn is looking for new recruits.

Chapter 8: "New Recruits"

Chapter 9: "The Blessingway"

Chapter 10: "Boot Camp"

Name _____

Date _____ Class _____

Chapter 11: "Code School"

_____

_____

_____

Chapter 12: "Learning the Code"

_____

_____

_____

Chapter 13: "Shipping Out to Hawaii"

_____

_____

_____

Chapter 14: "The Enemies"

_____

_____

_____

Chapter 15: "Field Maneuvers"

_____

_____

_____

Chapter 16: "Bombardment"

_____

_____

_____

Chapter 17: "First Landing"

_____

_____

_____

Chapter 18: "On Bougainville"

_____

_____

_____

Chapter 19: "Do You Have a Navajo?"

_____

_____

_____

Chapter 20: "The Next Targets"

_____

_____

_____

Name _____

Date _____ Class _____

Chapter 21: "Guam"

_____

_____

_____

Chapter 22: "Fatigue"

_____

_____

_____

Chapter 23: "Pavavu"

_____

_____

_____

Chapter 24: "Iwo Jima"

_____

_____

_____

Chapter 25: "In Sight of Suribachi"

_____

_____

_____

Chapter 26: "The Black Beach"

_____

_____

_____

Chapter 27: "Okinawa"

_____

_____

_____

Chapter 28: "The Bomb"

_____

_____

_____

Chapter 29: "Going Home"

_____

_____

_____

Name _____

Date _____ Class _____

Handout 9B: Ned Begay, Navajo and Marine

Directions: Use this handout to record evidence to show how Bruchac develops the central idea that specific elements of Ned's Navajo identity make him both want to join the Marines and be well qualified to serve as a Marine.

Ned's Navajo Identity	Ned's Desire, and Qualifications, to Be a Marine

Name _____

Date _____ Class _____

Handout 9C: Frayer Model

Directions: Take notes during class discussion of the target word, *motto*. Then in groups of three, brainstorm *mottos* that fit the criteria for each definition, and record them in the "Examples" box. Under "Non-Examples," record the displayed anti-proverbs along with their original phrasing.

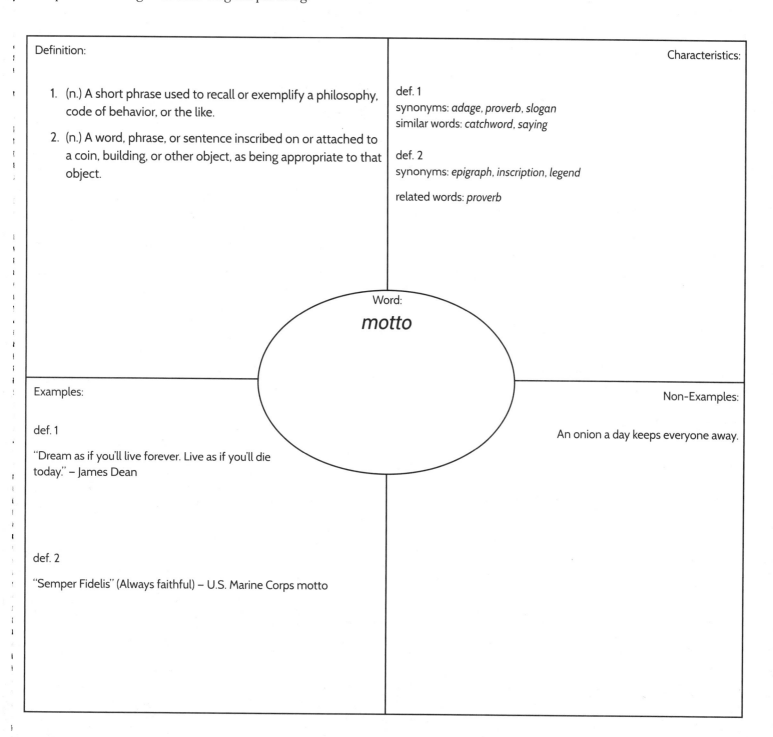

Definition:

1. (n.) A short phrase used to recall or exemplify a philosophy, code of behavior, or the like.

2. (n.) A word, phrase, or sentence inscribed on or attached to a coin, building, or other object, as being appropriate to that object.

Characteristics:

def. 1
synonyms: *adage, proverb, slogan*
similar words: *catchword, saying*

def. 2
synonyms: *epigraph, inscription, legend*

related words: *proverb*

Word:
motto

Examples:

def. 1

"Dream as if you'll live forever. Live as if you'll die today." – James Dean

def. 2

"Semper Fidelis" (Always faithful) – U.S. Marine Corps motto

Non-Examples:

An onion a day keeps everyone away.

Name _____

Date _____ Class _____

Handout 10A: Examining Style

Directions: Read the following two paragraphs, taking note of the differences between the two.

Paragraph 1

One great weapon that the U. S. armed forces used during World War II was called the MK 2 grenade. It was also known as the MK II. It was issued to all soldiers and was designed to fling deadly pieces of metal when it went off. Experts called it a fragmentation type anti-personnel hand grenade. Grooves put on the iron casing are what made it come apart. They also helped a soldier hold onto and throw the grenade. Funny thing is, the MK II looked like a pineapple because of those grooves, so soldiers called it a pineapple. But never mind the fruity nickname. The grenade was supposed to cause the enemy really bad injuries. But the MK II also had its problems, including failing to go off when it got moisture in it and stuff. You couldn't really depend on it. Maybe it would work or maybe not. So, the U.S. got a new and improved model later on.

Paragraph 2

During World War II, the U.S. armed forces employed a weapon called the MK 2 grenade, or the MK II. This standard-issue weapon was a fragmentation type anti-personnel hand grenade designed to disperse lethal fragments of metal on detonation. Heavy grooves in the cast-iron casing enhanced fragmentation and provided a better grip for handling and throwing the grenade. As a result of these grooves, the weapon closely resembled a pineapple, and soldiers often referred to the weapon as such. Despite having such an innocent-sounding nickname, the unique design of the grenade ensured optimum bodily harm to the enemy. Nevertheless, the MK II equally posed problems during combat, including its vulnerability to moisture and resulting failure to detonate. Due to its unreliability, the U.S. military replaced the grenade with a more reliable model sometime after World War II.

Name

Date   Class

Handout 11A: Central Ideas: Chapter 10

Directions: Think about the central ideas that Joseph Bruchac develops in chapter 10. In the table below, the left-hand column lists key events in chapter 10. In the corresponding rows of the right-hand column, describe why each event is important. What does it mean, and what central idea does it develop? (The first row has been completed as an example.) Then, answer the question below.

Chapter 10 Plot Event	What It Means / Central Idea It Supports
The recruits take the bus to be sworn in and are reminded of a journey that their ancestors made.	*This scene shows the strength of the Navajos' loyalty to their land that they are enlisting despite how they were treated in the past by the government.*
The Navajo find that boot camp does not seem as difficult for them as it does for others.	
Georgia Boy does not know how to read, and asks Ned to read his letter from home.	
Ned and Georgia Boy become friends.	

Wrap Up: What is a theme that is developed in chapter 10?

_____

_____

_____

_____

Name _____

Date _____ Class _____

Handout 11B: Examining Transitions

Directions: Insert appropriate transitions (words, phrases, or clauses) to better link the ideas in the following paragraph.

Ned discovers that despite being taught in boarding school that Navajos are inferior, his Navajo background is tremendously valuable. "What most young men found challenging was easy for us Indians" (61). Many men struggle to hike in the sun carrying heavy packs. They get sick from running. Ned and the other Navajos are used to walking twenty miles to the trading post and back, often carrying hundred-pound bags of flour. "No matter what it was…we Navajos were just about the best" (61). Ned becomes friends with Georgia Boy and promises to teach him to read. Ned begins to truly understand that whites are not superior to Navajos.

Name _____

Date _____   Class _____

Handout 12A: Boarding School/Code School Comparison

Directions: Complete the table to compare Ned's experiences in boarding school and code school. The first row shows an example. After completing the table, analyze the impact of Ned's experiences on his identify.

Boarding School Experience	Code School Experience	Same (=) or Different (≠)
Ned is told Navajo is a useless language.	*Ned is told that Navajo can be used as a secret code to save lives.*	
Ned is taken to a place with no idea what to expect or what might happen.		
	Ned's teachers are other Navajos.	
	Ned has both American Indian and non-Indian buddies.	
Ned is told to forget his culture and his Navajo way of life.		

How does Ned feel while he is at code-school training camp? (Write your response in complete sentences or as a list of adjectives that describe Ned.)

_____

_____

_____

How do Ned's experiences in chapters 11–12 influence his identity and sense of self?

_____

_____

_____

_____

_____

Name _____

Date _____ Class _____

Handout 12B: Fluency Homework

Directions:

1. Day 1: Read the text carefully, and annotate to help you read fluently.
2. Each day:
   a. Practice reading the text aloud three to five times.
   b. Evaluate your progress by placing a checkmark in the appropriate unshaded box.
   c. Ask someone (adult or peer) to listen and evaluate you as well.
3. Last day: Respond to the self-reflection questions at the end of this handout.

Code talker. It was the first time I had ever heard that name, but it sounded good to me. Then our two Navajo instructors began to explain our duties to us. The more they said, the better it sounded. Our job was to learn a new top-secret code based on the Navajo language. We would also be trained to be expert in every form of communication used by the Marine Corps, from radios to Morse code. Using our code, we could send battlefield messages that no one but another Navajo code talker could understand.

I realized right away that our job was a really important one. In order to win battles, Marines needed to communicate fast at long distances. In those days before computers, that meant using radio. However, anyone, including the Japanese, could listen to our radio messages. To keep messages secret, the Marines sent them in code. But the Japanese broke every code our American forces used. A new kind of code had to be created.

(Bruchac 73)

Student Performance Checklist:	Day 1		Day 2		Day 3		Day 4	
	You	Listener*	You	Listener	You	Listener*	You	Listener*
Accurately read the passage three to five times.								
Read with appropriate phrasing and pausing.								
Read with appropriate expression.								
Read articulately at a good pace, and an audible volume.								

*Adult or peer

Self-reflection: What choices did you make when deciding how to read this passage, and why? What would you like to improve on or try differently next time?

Name _____

Date _____ Class _____

Handout 12C: Transitional Phrases and Clauses Guide

Directions: Use these charts to develop your knowledge of transitional phrases and clauses and to help with your own writing. Then use them to analyze the examples in the table below.

Subordinate Conjunctions

when/time	place/setting	concession/contradiction	cause and effect
▪ after ▪ as ▪ before ▪ since ▪ until ▪ when ▪ whenever ▪ while	▪ where ▪ wherever	▪ although ▪ even if ▪ even though ▪ if ▪ though ▪ whether ▪ whereas	▪ because ▪ since ▪ so that ▪ why ▪ in order for

Prepositions

how	when/time	where/place				which
▪ according to ▪ along with ▪ apart from ▪ by means of ▪ together with ▪ in spite of ▪ instead of ▪ with ▪ without	▪ until ▪ after ▪ through ▪ as of ▪ before ▪ since ▪ during ▪ up/upon	▪ besides ▪ off ▪ between ▪ on top of ▪ beyond ▪ out ▪ by	▪ in front of ▪ around ▪ inside ▪ outside ▪ under ▪ over ▪ into ▪ behind	▪ near/nearby below ▪ next to ▪ up ▪ upon ▪ on ▪ across onto ▪ besides	▪ between ▪ beneath ▪ above ▪ against ▪ along ▪ alongside ▪ throughout ▪ in back of	▪ across from ▪ after ▪ of ▪ at

For the following sentences from *Code Talker*, complete the table with either an SC, if the sentence starts with a subordinate clause, or a PP, if the sentence starts with a prepositional phrase.

Sentences from *Code Talker*	SC or PP?
1. "As soon as we were finished, we were rounded up again and quickly marched to a building with bars on all the windows…" (Bruchac 70).	
2. "During World War One, our country had used other Indians, Cherokees and Chickasaws, to send messages in their own language to confuse the enemy" (74).	
3. "Because it was important for us to speak Navajo, we used it with each other much of the time" (81).	
4. "Near the end of our training, we decided to have a special Navajo dance…" (82).	

Name

Date   Class

Handout 12D: Transition Experimentation

Directions: Read the sentence pairs in the first two columns. Think about the transitional words and phrases you have discussed in the last two lessons. Use a transitional word or phrase to combine the sentences or to connect two separate sentences. (These might be subordinating clauses or prepositional phrases.) Write your new sentence, or sentences, in the third column. The first row has been completed as an example.

Sentence 1	Sentence 2	New Sentence
The Marines needed a new, unbreakable code.	They chose to use Navajo, a complex language known fully only to native speakers.	*(Cause-Effect Transition)* ▪ *The Marines needed a new, unbreakable code, and that is why they chose Navajo, a complex language known fully only to native speakers.*
1A. They thought they were going home on leave.	1B. They were surprised to find they were being sent to a new barracks for training.	*(Opposition/Contradiction Transition)*
2A. The instructors were speaking Navajo.	2B. They wanted Ned and the other Marines to speak Navajo.	*(Agreement/Addition Transition)*
3A. The Navajo were tough and determined Marines.	3B. They had suffered and had to work hard to prove themselves.	*(Cause-Effect Transition)*
4A. Navajo was one of the most difficult languages to learn.	4B. Very few non-Navajo spoke the language.	*(Agreement/Addition Transition)*
5A. They mastered the code.	5B. They had fun.	*(Time or Sequence Transition)*

Name _____

Date _____ Class _____

Handout 13A: Outside-In

Directions: Complete each part of the handout to consider the different meanings of the word *offensive*.

Part I: Outside – Examine

Group A

- The <u>offensive</u> by the Marines will begin at dawn tomorrow.
- Our team quickly planned a clever <u>offensive</u> and scored a touchdown.

Group B

- I'm angry because my sister made an <u>offensive</u> remark about me today.
- An <u>offensive</u> smell of rotten food penetrated the house the last time we forgot to take out the trash.

Group C

- The Marines executed an <u>offensive</u> military strategy and prevented a terrorist attack.
- To ensure a win, our team will take an <u>offensive</u> approach to today's game.

Group: **A**   **B**   **C**   (circle which group you are assigned in class)

- Step 1: Underline the context clues that show the meaning of the word *offensive* in your group of sentences.
- Step 2: Record the part of speech and meaning of *offensive* in your group of sentences.

offensive (_____): _____

_____

Part II: Outside – Experiment

Use the context clues to label each sentence A, B, or C to tell which meaning of *offensive* is used.

Sentence	A, B, or C
1. When he joined the Marines, Ned Begay probably did not have any idea what it would actually be like to be part of an offensive military attack.	
2. Part of the Japanese code of combat stated that they should always take the offensive.	
3. Ned's teachers made offensive comments to the Navajo students, but Ned chose to stay calm instead of losing his temper.	

Part III: Inside

Root Word	Meaning	Suffix	Meaning
offens–	An injury, an insult, a strike against.	*–ive*	Tending to; pertaining to; doing.

Brainstorm other words that share either the root or the suffix of the word *offensive*.

Name

Date   Class

Handout 14A: Word Exploration

Directions: Read the words and definitions below. On a separate piece of paper, show what the words mean in an alternative way–either by a picture, a sentence using the word in context, a comparison or analogy, or by breaking the word down into its parts. When possible, show how the word is used in *Code Talker*, with a related picture, sentence, or comparison.

Group 1: Compound Words	Definition
clockwork (104)	"Like clockwork" means something that happens easily and accurately; automatically; precisely.
crossfire (117)	A volley of gunfire directed at a central point from two different positions.
foxhole (117)	A shallow ditch dug quickly to protect from enemy fire.
minesweepers (109)	A naval vessel used for destroying, removing, or deactivating enemy mines.
outpost (107)	A military post that is a long distance from a main station.

Group 2: Multiple-Meaning Words	Definition
canteen (98)	A small portable container used for carrying water.
knot (103)	A speed equal to one nautical mile (6,080 feet) per hour.
post (112)	A position or duty that someone has been assigned to.
shell (104)	A cylindrical piece of ammunition, typically used in a shotgun.

Group 3: Sports-Related Words	Definition
defense (106)	Something that protects or defends.
exercise (98)	A military training operation or war game.
gung-ho (98)	Extremely enthusiastic and loyal.
maneuver (98)	A planned movement of military vehicles and troops.

Group 4: Weapons and Warfare Words	Definition
ammunition (110)	Objects that are detonated from any weapon.
bayonets (102)	A weapon like a knife that attaches to the end of a rifle for use in close combat.
bombardment (100)	An attack with bombs, canon fire, or gunfire.
shrapnel (117)	Metal pieces scattered by an exploding shell or bomb.

Group 5: Helpful Affix Words	Definition
amphibious (100)	Able to be used on both land and water.
division (100)	An administrative unit in the military.
neutralize (107)	To cause to be ineffective or become useless.
regiment (100)	A troop of soldiers made up of at least two battalions.

Group 6: More Helpful Affix Words	Definition
civilian (109)	A person who is not serving in the military.
portable (115)	Capable of being easily carried or transported.
reconnaissance (107)	The act of examining an area, especially to gain militarily useful information.
reinforcements (107)	Additions of materials or personnel to a military force.
transport (n.) (111)	A ship or plane used to carry supplies and military troops.

Name _____

Date _____   Class _____

Handout 14B: Examining Style and Tone

Directions: Read the following two paragraphs, noting the similarities and differences in style and tone between the two.

Paragraph 1

While trouble was brewing in the rest of the world, America had its own problems in the 1930s—it was stuck in a severe economic depression. Americans did not want to get involved in another "European mess," as they had during World War I (1914–1918). As President Franklin D. Roosevelt said, "We seek to isolate ourselves from war." But U.S. isolationism, a policy of not getting involved in the political or economic situations of other countries, came at a dangerous time. Building on the bitterness and bad conditions that resulted from Germany's loss in World War I, Adolf Hitler was rising to power in that country. By the mid-1930s, using violence and hatred to spread his fascist ideas, Hitler and the Nazi party had gained control of Germany. (Miller and Clemens, Handout 8C)

Paragraph 2

The recovery of the Navajo nation that took place over the next century and a half is so incredible that one might conclude that not only are the Navajos one of the most remarkable native nations that has ever existed but also that they have been truly blessed and protected by their Holy People. Today, the Navajo Reservation comprises 26,897 square miles. It is the largest Indian reservation in the United States. There are more than 200,000 Navajos. Although it is not without its problems and challenges, the Navajo nation has been described as one of the most economically prosperous and forward-looking of all the American Indian nations in the United States. Yet it is also true that a deep regard remains for the ancient traditions of Dinetah (Bruchac 217–218).

Name _____

Date _____   Class _____

Handout 14C: Tone Words

Directions: Use this list of tone words to complete the activities in Lesson 14. Keep the list as a reference for future assignments.

Positive Tone Words

amused	confident	hopeful	proud
appreciative	consoling	humorous	romantic
approving	content	joyful	supportive
authoritative	elated	optimistic	sympathetic
comical	encouraging	passionate	unconcerned
compassionate	enthusiastic	playful	understanding
complimentary	excited	pleased	whimsical
concerned	fascinated	positive	

Neutral Tone Words

academic	diplomatic	instructive	sentimental
authoritative	formal	neutral	unbiased
clinical	indifferent	nostalgic	unconcerned
detached	informative	objective	

Negative Tone Words

accusatory	cynical	indecisive	sad
aggravated	desperate	indignant	sarcastic
agitated	disappointed	insolent	satiric
angry	disdainful	insulting	scornful
annoyed	disgruntled	irreverent	serious
apathetic	disgusted	irritated	shameful
belligerent	disinterested	malicious	sharp
bitter	dismissive	mocking	snooty
brash	displeased	negative	sober
cold	facetious	offensive	solemn
concerned	fickle	outraged	superior
condemning	flippant	overconfident	surly
condescending	frustrated	passive	taunting
contemptuous	furious	patronizing	testy
contradictory	harsh	pompous	threatening
course	hateful	resentful	uninterested
critical	haughty	ridiculing	wrathful

Name _____

Date _____ Class _____

Handout 16A: Fluency Homework

Directions:

1 Day 1: Read the text carefully, and annotate to help you read fluently.

2 Each day:

    a Practice reading the text aloud three to five times.

    b Evaluate your progress by placing a checkmark in the appropriate unshaded box.

    c Ask someone (adult or peer) to listen and evaluate you as well.

3 Last day: Respond to the self-reflection questions at the end of this handout.

Our war in the Pacific was so different from the one fought in Europe. In Europe, when our enemies saw they were losing a battle, they would often surrender. Sometimes tens of thousands of prisoners would be taken. I saw newsreels of long lines of defeated German soldiers, just peacefully walking away from the battle, guarded by only a few Americans. They were abiding by the rules of war. How I wished that the Japanese would behave that way. Their rules, though, were different.

You see, grandchildren, rules about modern warfare were made up between the nations of the world before World War Two. Those rules said that prisoners of war, enemy soldiers who had surrendered or been captured, had to be fed and housed in a humane way. They had to be allowed visits by the Red Cross. Those rules, called the Geneva convention, were agreed to in 1929 and signed by almost every major nation. But not the Japanese. They had different ideas about war. They had been taught since childhood that retreating, surrendering, or being captured in war was a great shame to your nation and family. A Japanese soldier was supposed to die in banzai charges or kill himself rather than give up. Anyone taken captive by the Japanese was scorned as a coward.

(Bruchac 168–169)

Student Performance Checklist:	Day 1		Day 2		Day 3		Day 4	
	You	Listener*	You	Listener	You	Listener*	You	Listener*
Accurately read the passage three to five times.								
Read with appropriate phrasing and pausing.								
Read with appropriate expression.								
Read articulately at a good pace, and an audible volume.								

*Adult or peer

Self-reflection: What choices did you make when deciding how to read this passage, and why? What would you like to improve on or try differently next time?

Name _____

Date _____ Class _____

Handout 17A: Content, Style, and Structure

Directions: Answer the questions to analyze content, style, and structure in chapters 24–26 of *Code Talker*.

1 How does the author, Bruchac, **foreshadow**, or warn of, the horrors of Iwo Jima in chapters 24 and 25? One example is provided for you. Name two more examples.

Example: When Ned Begay hears the name, a "cold feeling went down [his] spine. [He] wondered if it was because [he] was going to die there" (173).

1

_____

_____

_____

2

_____

_____

_____

2 In chapters 24–26, how does Bruchac continue to develop the **central idea** that Ned's culture sustains him during difficult and challenging times? One example is provided for you. Name two more examples.

Example: His Navajo spiritual beliefs make him feel stronger. Before he goes into battle, Ned goes to the upper deck to be closer to the sky. He places pollen on his head and tongue, and prays to his Holy People.

1

_____

_____

_____

_____

2

_____

_____

_____

_____

3 In chapters 24–26, Bruchac uses **contrast** to describe Iwo Jima, such as when he writes "what had seemed like a walk in the park had turned into a swim in sea of fire" (183). Name two more examples of how Bruchac contrasts the idea of a paradise or a dream with a nightmare or hell.

1

_____

_____

_____

_____

2

_____

_____

_____

_____

Name _____

Date _____ Class _____

4   When Ned reaches the top of the slope of black sand on the beach, Bruchac writes: "Our work was worth it, though. When we finally reached the top a big reward was waiting for us. Not only did we have a great view, but we were fully exposed to the enemy fire that started the exact instant the two of us got there" (184–185). Describe Bruchac's tone. Why do you think he chooses to use this **tone**?

_____

_____

_____

_____

5   Reread pages 186–187, starting with "When I think of that time, scattered pictures appear" and ending with "our voices held it together." Analyze the author's **content**, **style**, and **structure** in these paragraphs.

Be sure to describe the author's:

- Development of the central idea: that Ned's Navajo identity sustains him in times of challenge.

- Inclusion of sensory details: sights, smells, and sounds.

- Use of contrast to describe and highlight important ideas.

- Use of images (the net and the web).

_____

_____

_____

_____

_____

_____

_____

_____

_____

_____

Name _____

Date _____   Class _____

Handout 18A: "Navajo Code Talkers"

Directions: Read this article to learn more about the Navajo code talkers.

Navajo Code Talkers
by Harry Gardiner

1   When Japanese planes attacked Pearl Harbor on the morning of December 7, 1941, most members of the United States' largest Indian tribe were isolated from the problems of the day. When they heard the news, though, they picked up their guns and headed for the nearest recruiting station. In New Mexico, one group of fighting men cleaned and oiled their rifles, packed their saddlebags, and rode off to Gallup, ready to do battle with the enemy.

2   More than three thousand Navajo would eventually serve their country throughout the world. They would be found in the Aleutian Islands, in North Africa, on the Normandy beaches, in Italy and Sicily, and, most of all, in the Central and South Pacific. They were better prepared to deal with conditions on the Pacific islands than most U.S. soldiers. For example, they could crawl through the jungle without making noise, hiding behind bushes their Anglo comrades had not even noticed. Because they were used to desert darkness instead of lighted streets, they were able to move around in the dark with great accuracy in almost any kind of terrain. They often amazed their white companions with their ability to spot a snake by smell or sound.

3   Those who did not enter military service contributed in a variety of ways at home by working in ports building ships, in munitions plants, for the Red Cross, or for the Bureau of Indian Affairs. Many Navajo women served in the Women's Army Corps as cooks, weather forecasters, nurses, and nutritionists.

4   One man, Philip Johnston, a civil engineer from Los Angeles, changed the lives of many young Navajo men in a unique way. The son of a missionary father, Johnston had spent a large part of his early life living among the Navajo and spoke their language fluently. This was not easy to do, since the language is extremely complex, very difficult to learn, and nearly impossible to imitate. Johnston proposed that the Marine Corps use a code based on the Navajo language to prevent Japanese and German cryptographers from decoding U.S. messages. His plan was approved, and during the next five years, he helped turn more than four hundred Navajo into Marine "code talkers" and the Navajo language into one of the United States' more successful secret weapons.

5   The Navajo were chosen for several reasons. First, Johnston had an intimate knowledge of their language and culture. Second, the tribe was big enough to provide a large number of speakers. Third, only twenty-eight non-Navajo, mainly missionaries and anthropologists, could speak the language—and none of these was Japanese or German.

6   The Navajo language developed over many centuries, making it very complex. For example, the same word spoken with four different alterations in pitch or tone of voice has four different meanings. Depending on how you pronounce the Navajo word written ni, it can have meanings as different as "A set of round objects extends off in a horizontal line" and "I bought it." This complexity, combined with fluent speakers who could transmit the code more quickly than an artificial code, made it difficult to decode.

7   Because it might fall into enemy hands, this new code was to be spoken only over the radio or telephone and never to be put into writing. Since the plan was to develop a code of Indian words, not merely to use translations of Indian words, there had to be complete agreement on the meanings of all words used. Any variation in interpretation could spell disaster.

8   The code talkers had to memorize the entire vocabulary of 411 terms. In competitions with Anglo marines, the Navajo code talkers always won in both speed and accuracy. Even the most complicated reports and instructions were transmitted without a single error—an achievement that regular communications men speaking in code were unable to duplicate. The code was so successful that the Japanese and Germans failed to decipher a single syllable of the thousands of messages sent with it.

9   In the September 18, 1945, issue of the *San Diego Union*, it was stated, "For three years, wherever the Marines landed, the Japanese got an earful of strange gurgling noises interspersed with other sounds resembling the call of a Tibetan monk and the sound of a hot water bottle being emptied."

10   The importance of the role played by the Navajo code talkers was noted by Major Howard Conner when he said, "Were it not for the Navajos, the Marines would never have taken Iwo Jima!" The capture of this island was crucial to U.S. forces in the last stages of the war because Japanese planes had continually attacked U.S. bombers from there. The entire military operation was directed by Navajo code talkers. During the first forty-eight hours, they sent and received more than eight hundred messages without error. When the famous flag raising took place on Mount Suribachi, the news came in the Navajo code, with the Japanese name of Suribachi pronounced as Sheep-uncle-ram-ice-bear-ant-cat-horse-itch.

11   After the war, some of the code talkers went to work for the Bureau of Indian Affairs. Others found work as interpreters, engineers, and construction supervisors. Still others continued their education and became teachers, lawyers, and doctors.

12   Navajo code remained a secret until 1965. In March 1989, the surviving code talkers were reunited in Phoenix, Arizona, and honored by the commandant of the Marine Corps. A statue was unveiled at the ceremony.

Name _____

Date _____ Class _____

The Navajo Code
by Harry Gardiner

Military Term	Navajo Word	Navajo Meaning
Corps	Din-neh-ih	Clan
Squad	Debeh-li-zini	Black sheet
Colonel	Atsah-besh-le-gai	Silver eagle
Dive bomber	Gini	Chicken hawk
Observation plane	Ne-as-jah	Owl
Battleship	Lo-tso	Whale
Submarine	Besh-lo	Iron fish
Minesweeper	Cha	Beaver
January	Yas-nil-tes	Crusted snow
Bombs	A-ye-shi	Eggs
Engineer	Day-dil-jah-hi	Fire builder
Grenades	Ni-ma-si	Potatoes

To test the usefulness of the code, Navajo not in the code program were sent into the field to try to decipher messages sent with these words. Even though all these words were part of their native language, without knowing the special meanings, they were unsuccessful.

Citation: Gardiner, Harry. "Navajo Code Talkers." Cobblestone. Cobblestone Publishing Co. 1989.

Name _____

Date _____ Class _____

Handout 18B: Informational Text Analysis

Directions: Annotate these paragraphs from "Navajo Code Talkers" (Handout 18A) to examine the elements of effective informational text.

1 Topic Statement: Underline the topic statement.

2 Evidence: Place a checkmark (✓) before a sentence if it provides evidence.

3 Elaboration: Write a plus sign (+) before a sentence if it provides elaboration.

4 Concluding Statement: Underline the concluding statement.

5 Transitions: Circle any transition words.

6 Word Choice and Style: Double underline three examples of effective word choice or formal style.

A few annotations have been made to get you started.

[Paragraph 4] One man, Philip Johnston, a civil engineer from Los Angeles, changed the lives of many young Navajo men in a unique way. The son of a missionary father, Johnston had spent a large part of his early life living among the Navajo and spoke their language fluently. + This was not easy to do, since the language is extremely complex, very difficult to learn, and nearly impossible to imitate. ✓ Johnston proposed that the Marine Corps use a code based on the Navajo language to prevent Japanese and German cryptographers from decoding U.S. messages. His plan was approved, and during the next five years, he helped turn more than four hundred Navajo into Marine "code talkers" and the Navajo language into one of the United States' more successful secret weapons.

[Paragraph 5] The Navajo were chosen for several reasons. (First,) Johnston had an intimate knowledge of their language and culture. Second, the tribe was big enough to provide a large number of speakers. Third, only twenty-eight non-Navajo, mainly missionaries and anthropologists, could speak the language—and none of these was Japanese or German.

[Paragraph 6] The Navajo language developed over many centuries, making it very complex. For example, the same word spoken with four different alterations in pitch or tone of voice has four different meanings. Depending on how you pronounce the Navajo word written ni', it can have meanings as different as "A set of round objects extends off in a horizontal line" and "I bought it." This complexity, combined with fluent speakers who could transmit the code more quickly than an artificial code, made it difficult to decode.

Now, look at the concluding statement to the article "Navajo Code Talkers." What sentence can you add to the end of the essay to give the reader perspective or end with a final, important thought about the code talkers?

_____

_____

_____

_____

Name _____

Date _____ Class _____

Handout 19A: Before, During, and After Chart

Directions: Ned Begay's experiences and interactions with non-Navajos are very different during the different periods of his life. Use this table to describe his experience before, during, and after the war.

Before the War: In Boarding School	During the War: As a Marine	After the War: Back Home

Name _____

Date _____ Class _____

Handout 19B: Speaking and Listening Goal-Setting and Self-Assessment

Directions: Use this tool to set a goal for and assess your participation in the Socratic Seminar.

Before the Discussion: Set a Goal

My goal for this discussion is to:

After the Discussion: Self-Assess

Criteria	+/ Δ *
I came prepared for the discussion.	
I posed questions.	
I responded to questions.	
I made relevant observations.	
I acknowledged and built on others' ideas.	
I listened carefully.	
I brought the discussion back on topic as needed.	
I agreed and disagreed respectfully.	
▪ I did not interrupt.	
▪ I used a polite tone of voice.	
▪ I disagreed with the statement, not the person.	
I used appropriate, formal, academic language. For example:	
I used vocabulary that I learned in this module, such as these words:	

* (+ = Good performance   Δ = Needs improvement)

I met my goal for this discussion.   YES   /   NO

Explain:

My goal for the next discussion is to:

_____

_____

_____

_____

Name

Date   Class

Handout 20A: ToSEEC Paragraph Organizer

Directions: Use the organizer to plan for your Focusing Question Task 2 response.

Topic Statement:

Evidence	Elaboration

Evidence	Elaboration

Concluding Statement

Name _____

Date _____ Class _____

Handout 21A: Checklist for Focusing Question Task 2

Directions: Use this checklist to review your own or a classmate's Focusing Question Task 2 response.

Writer:	Reviewer:

ToSEEC Structure

Does the paragraph include:

_____ A clear topic statement, stating one Navajo belief or way of life that supports the protagonist?

_____ Evidence (from several different places in the book and including quotations from *Code Talker*) of how the author develops the idea that this belief or way of life supports him?

_____ Elaboration that explains how the evidence develops the topic?

_____ A concluding statement that reinforces the essential idea?

Cohesion

Does the paragraph demonstrate:

_____ A logical organization?

Language and Style

Does the writer use:

_____ Precise language, including two words from the module's Vocabulary Journal entries?

_____ A formal style (no slang, no contractions) appropriate to purpose and audience?

Conventions of Writing

Does the writer:

_____ Spell correctly?

_____ Punctuate correctly?

_____ Use correct grammar and avoid sentence fragments?

Name _____

Date _____   Class _____

Handout 21B: ToSEEC Paragraph Structure Review

Directions: Use this review sheet to review your own or a classmate's Focusing Question Task 2 response.

Writer:	Reviewer:

Topic Statement: Underline the topic statement.

Does the topic statement clearly state one Navajo belief or way of life that supports Ned Begay?   Y   N

If No, how can it be improved?

Does the topic statement engage the reader?   Y   N

If No, how can it be improved?

Evidence: Write a checkmark (✓) to identify evidence.

Does the evidence support the topic? Is it relevant?   Y   N

If No, what evidence should be taken out?

Is the evidence sufficient? Does it come from more than one place in *Code Talker*?   Y   N

If No, what other evidence is needed to support the topic?

Elaboration: Write a plus sign (+) to mark elaboration.

Does the paragraph include elaboration?   Y   N

If No, what should be added to clarify or explain ideas?

Does the elaboration clarify and explain ideas?   Y   N

If No, how can it be improved?

Concluding Statement: Underline the concluding statement.

Does the concluding statement reinforce the essential idea of the paragraph?   Y   N

If No, how can it be improved?

Writer:	Reviewer:

Overall:

Does the paragraph respond to the prompt in Assessment 20A? Y N

If No, what part of the prompt is not addressed?

Does the paragraph answer the reader's questions? Y N

If No, what other questions should the writer answer?

What is one strength of this paragraph?

Name _____

Date _____ Class _____

Handout 23A: "Relocation Camps"

Directions: Read this article to learn more about the Japanese internment camps of World War II.

Relocation Camps
by Craig E. Blohm

1   Seven-year-old Jeanne Wakatsuki watched wide-eyed as the California countryside rolled past the windows of the Greyhound bus. She was excited, for this was her first bus ride. But what little Jeanne did not know was her ultimate destination, a relocation camp called Manzanar. It was the early days of World War II, and for the United States and its Japanese citizens, a sad chapter of history was beginning.

2   Japanese immigration to the United States had begun in the late 1800s. Japanese citizens left their homeland in hopes of finding a better life in this country. But unlike the European immigrants who preceded them, the Japanese brought with them customs that seemed strange to Americans. Emperor worship and Shintoism, a religion in which the dead are revered, were difficult for Americans to understand. Before long, racial discrimination against the Japanese began, especially on the West Coast where most of the immigrants had settled. This unfortunate situation was made worse on the morning of December 7, 1941.

3   *We interrupt this program to bring you a special news bulletin. The Japanese have attacked Pearl Harbor!*

4   With this brief radio announcement, most Americans learned of the bombing of Pearl Harbor. Overnight, fear of another attack set in. People wondered whether Los Angeles or San Francisco might be the next target. As if by reflex action, anti-Japanese hatred exploded. Although most were American citizens, Japanese Americans could no longer cash checks at their banks. Milk deliveries to Japanese American households stopped, and it became difficult for them to buy groceries. Soon an ominous fear surfaced in the minds of many Americans: Could these Japanese Americans be spies? Might they try to sabotage our military installations? Newspaper editorials echoed this disturbing sentiment: Get rid of the "Japs"!

5   Many Japanese Americans tried to prove their loyalty to America. The Japanese American Citizens League sent a telegram to President Franklin D. Roosevelt, affirming the league's allegiance to the United States. But the fear had become too great for even President Roosevelt to resist. On February 19, 1942, the president signed Executive Order 9066. By this decree, all Japanese Americans living on the West Coast were to be removed from their homes and put into relocation, or concentration, camps.

6   When Jeanne Wakatsuki stepped off the bus at the Manzanar relocation center, a bleak vista awaited her. Row after row of wood and tarpaper barracks stood on the barren desert floor. Barbed-wire fences ringed the camp, with high wooden watchtowers looming overhead. Inside, the barracks were divided into six large rooms, one for each family of evacuees. A bare light bulb hanging from the ceiling, an oil-burning furnace, and a few cots were the only furnishings. Large gaps between the floorboards allowed the ever-present desert dust to enter the barracks on windy days. Privacy was almost nonexistent, and bathroom and laundry facilities were housed in a separate building. Evacuees had few belongings, for they were allowed to take to the camps only what they could carry.

7   In all, there were ten relocation centers, each housing between five thousand and sixteen thousand people. Most were located in the western United States, but two were built as far away as Arkansas. All were similar to Manzanar, constructed in deserts or other desolate areas.

8   Despite the many hardships, the evacuees made the best of their situation. Slowly the relocation centers became self-contained, organized towns. The people planted flower and vegetable gardens and furnished the bare rooms with mail-order bedspreads and curtains. Unused barracks became schools, with classes ranging from nursery school to adult education. Camp recreation included boxing, Ping-Pong, and baseball (at some camps as many as one hundred baseball teams were organized). Most centers had libraries and published community newspapers.

9   Although life in the camps reached some degree of normality, it was not without conflict. The stress of so many people living closely under poor housing conditions caused occasional violence. Tension also grew between the Issei (older evacuees who were born in Japan) and the Nisei (younger, American-born Japanese). Arguments about the advantages of the Nisei's American citizenship were frequent, sometimes bitterly dividing families. On one occasion, riots between the two groups broke out at Manzanar.

Name _____

Date _____ Class _____

10   In late 1942, more than one hundred thousand Japanese Americans were living in relocation centers, but the face of the war was beginning to change. Japanese forces had been defeated at the battle of Midway, and it soon became obvious that the United States' mainland was no longer vulnerable to a Japanese attack. In short, there was no longer a reason to keep Japanese Americans behind the barbed wire of the relocation camps.

11   Unfortunately, because of many delays, some of them politically motivated, an official end to the camps did not come until two years later. In December 1944, the relocation camps ended as they had begun, by presidential decree. Slowly, American citizens, imprisoned solely because of their race, left the camps and returned to an uncertain freedom.

12   Of course, the United States was not the only nation to build concentration camps during World War II. Hitler's Nazis constructed more than one hundred camps devoted to the destruction of European Jews and other people Hitler deemed undesirable. (This destruction was known as the Holocaust.) Even today, the names Auschwitz, Dachau, and Bergen-Belsen stir up grim memories. Although American concentration camps might seem humane in comparison, they remain a dark spot on the pages of our history.

Citation: Blohm, Craig E. "Relocation Camps." Cricket Media.

Name

Date   Class

Handout 24A: Transition Revision

Directions: With a partner, identify and annotate opportunities in the paragraph below to include transitions, and then revise the paragraph to include effective transitions.

Jeanne Wakatsuki's father disappeared. She claims that it didn't bother her nearly as much as the world she eventually found herself in. Jeanne and her family lived in Ocean Park near Santa Monica, a block away from the beach. They were the only Japanese family in the neighborhood, and Jeanne's father liked it that way. Jeanne believes he didn't want to be labeled or grouped by anyone. Jeanne's mother moved the family down to Terminal Island. The island was a country as foreign as India or Arabia would have been. It was the first time that she had lived among other Japanese or gone to school with them. She was terrified much of the time.

_____

_____

_____

_____

_____

_____

Name _____

Date _____ Class _____

Handout 25A: Tableau Planning Sheet

Directions: Plan a precise Tableau that represents a family memory or key moment in the Wakatsukis' early days at Manzanar. Write your scene number here: Scene _____ .

	What should this person's positioning and facial expression look like?	Explanation for the pose: What are they feeling in this moment?	Evidence: What quotation supports your choices?
Character 1: _____			
Character2: _____			
Character 3: _____			
Character 4: _____			

Select a quotation from the text to be your Tableau's caption:

_____

_____

_____

Explain what the caption reveals about how the internment affected individuals at Manzanar.

_____

_____

_____

Name _____

Date _____ Class _____

Handout 27A: Photography Analysis

Directions: Read the following terms and draw an example. Later in the lesson, you will use this handout to analyze Ansel Adams's photos.

Visual Art Terms	Quick Sketch
Elements of Art – The basic tools artists use to make a work of art; *line, color, shape* **or** *form*, *texture*, **and** *space* **are the six elements of art.**	
Line: a mark made by drawing with a pencil or paintbrush. Line is the basic building block of art and can be used to make more complicated shapes or lead the viewers' eyes to a certain point or area.	
Value: how light or dark a color looks. White is the lightest value; black is the darkest.	
Shape **– An area bounded by a line. Artists may use** *geometric* **or** *organic* **shapes in their work.**	
Geometric shape: a shape with even sides, curves, or edges such as a circle, square, or triangle.	
Organic shape: a shape that seems to come from nature, with uneven edges and sides.	
Principles of Art – Different ways the elements of art are combined in a work of art.	
Movement: how artists use line, color, or shapes to move your eye around a work of art.	
Pattern: a regular, repeated design. For example, artists may create patterns through repeating vertical or horizontal lines. Pattern can create movement.	

Balance – A way of organizing the shapes and colors in a work of art so that the sides appear even. The three types of balance are *symmetrical*, *asymmetrical*, and *radial*.	
Symmetrical balance: the work of art is equally weighted on both sides of a central line.	
Asymmetrical balance: the work of art is unevenly weighted.	
Radial balance: the weight moves out from a center point in a work of art.	
Other Terms	
Contrast: when an artist puts things that look different next to each other. Artists can contrast two or more colors, textures, lines, or shapes.	
Frame: refers to what is included in the photograph.	

Handout 27B: Fluency Homework

Directions:

1 Day 1: Read the text carefully, and annotate to help you read fluently.

2 Each day:

   a Practice reading the text aloud three to five times.

   b Evaluate your progress by placing a checkmark in the appropriate unshaded box.

   c Ask someone (adult or peer) to listen and evaluate you as well.

3 Last day: Respond to the self-reflection questions at the end of this handout.

"...you must believe in what you're fighting for. If you do not believe, you will not be willing to die. If you are not willing to die, you won't fight well. And if you don't fight well you will probably be killed stupidly, for the wrong reason, and unheroically. So tell me, how can you think of going off to fight?"

Woody always answered softly, respectfully, with a boyish and submissive smile.

"I will fight well, Papa."

"In this war? How is it possible?"

"I am an American citizen. America is at war."

"But look where they have put us!"

"The more of us who go into the army, the sooner the war will be over, the sooner you and Mama will be out of here."

"Do you think I would risk losing a son for that?"

(Wakatsuki Houston 75)

Student Performance Checklist:	Day 1		Day 2		Day 3		Day 4	
	You	Listener*	You	Listener	You	Listener*	You	Listener*
Accurately read the passage three to five times.								
Read with appropriate phrasing and pausing.								
Read with appropriate expression.								
Read articulately at a good pace, and an audible volume.								

*Adult or peer

Self-reflection: What choices did you make when deciding how to read this passage, and why? What would you like to improve on or try differently next time?

Name _____

Date _____ Class _____

Handout 29A: Content Vocabulary Word Relationships

Directions: Use the information in the Vocabulary Chart to complete this activity with a partner. In the Word Relationships Map, note any relationships among the words that you can.

Vocabulary Chart

Word	Meaning	Synonyms
prevail (v.)	To emerge as dominant (often followed by "over").	overcome, predominate, triumph
strive (v.)	To try or work hard toward a goal; to exert oneself.	endeavor, strain, struggle, try
endure (v.)	To bear up under adversity or to function in spite of it.	persevere, withstand

Word Relationships Map

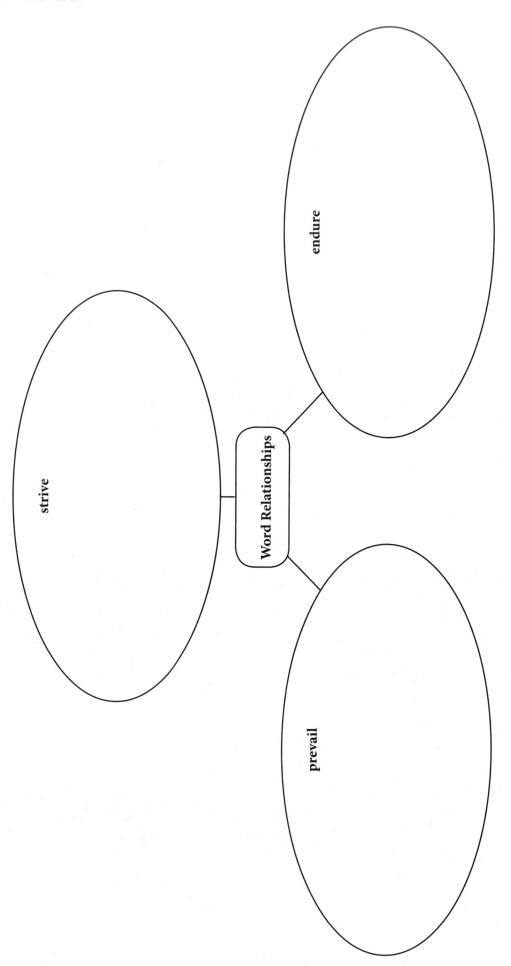

endure

strive

Word Relationships

prevail

Name

Date   Class

Handout 30A: Speaking and Listening Goal-Setting and Self-Assessment

Directions: Use this tool to set a goal for and assess your participation in the Socratic Seminar.

Before the Discussion: Set a Goal

My goal for this discussion is to:

After the Discussion: Self-Assess

Criteria	+/ Δ *
I came prepared for the discussion.	
I posed questions.	
I responded to questions.	
I made relevant observations.	
I acknowledged and built on others' ideas.	
I listened carefully.	
I brought the discussion back on topic as needed.	
I agreed and disagreed respectfully.	
▪ I did not interrupt.	
▪ I used a polite tone of voice.	
▪ I disagreed with the statement, not the person.	
I used appropriate, formal, academic language. For example:	
I used vocabulary that I learned in this module, such as these words:	

* (+ = Good performance   Δ = Needs improvement)

I met my goal for this discussion.   YES   /   NO

Explain:

My goal for the next discussion is to:

_____

_____

_____

_____

Name _____

Date _____ Class _____

Handout 30B: Central Idea Analysis

Directions: Identify two central ideas from *Farewell to Manzanar*, and record evidence that demonstrates how Wakatsuki Houston develops each of these ideas over the course of the text.

	Earlier in the Text	Later in the Text
Central Idea 1:	How does this idea emerge? Textual evidence:	How does this idea unfold? Textual evidence:

Central Idea 2:	How does this idea emerge?	How does this idea unfold?
	Textual evidence:	Textual evidence:

Name _____

Date _____ Class _____

Handout 30C: Using Modifying Phrases and Clauses

Directions: Read each of the following sentences, which are based on chapter 29 of *Code Talker*, for meaning. Then incorporate the specified phrases and clauses so that they modify the appropriate subject or word in each sentence. Be sure to punctuate and capitalize your revised sentences correctly.

1 Ned and his fellow soldiers kept their code a secret until the operation was declassified.
   • respecting their military orders

   _____

   _____

2 The code talkers' occupational specialty was not mentioned on their discharge papers.
   • protected under military law

   _____

   _____

3 Specialties noted were professions that were needed back home.
   • in soldiers' discharge papers

   _____

   _____

4 There was a special number assigned.
   • for each type of work

   _____

   _____

5 Ned was able to discuss the top-secret occupation he held with the U.S. Marine Corps.
   • only after it was declassified

   _____

   _____

Name _____

Date _____ Class _____

Handout 32A: Informative Essay Model

Directions: Evaluate the model using the Checklist for Success from your EOM Task prompt. For each criterion, annotate textual examples.

Prompt (different from your EOM Task!): Individuals responded to the challenges of World War II in many different ways. Select an individual from *Farewell to Manzanar*, and explain how he or she responded to the war's challenges. Your purpose is to demonstrate your understanding of responses to the war. Your audience is your teacher and classmates.

Wartime Woody Wakatsuki

Being a big brother is never easy. Top that off with a race-based forced relocation to a concentration camp, and I would say you have earned the right to complain. In Jeanne Wakatsuki Houston's memoir, *Farewell to Manzanar*, however, brother Woody Wakatsuki never does! After Japan bombed Pearl Harbor, the U.S. government feared Japanese Americans might be disloyal, so they imprisoned Woody's family and thousands of others at Manzanar Internment Camp. Internees responded to this injustice in diverse ways. Woody responded in a manner that reflected his unique personality. Woody chose to express a positive attitude in order to help his family endure. He also chose to serve in the U.S. Army.

Woody chose to maintain a positive attitude in order to help his family endure a painful wartime experience. The Wakatsukis' first day at Manzanar was difficult because they had been separated from Papa, it was cold, and their living conditions were appalling. Mama was distraught. Woody responded by smiling, hugging her tight, and saying "We'll make it better, Mama. You watch" (24), although "Grief flickered in his eyes" (24). This shows that inwardly, Woody felt upset. Instead of expressing it, though, he comforted his mother and provided hope. After they were served terrible food, Woody joked that their next meal would be rice with syrup. This would taste even more terrible, and Woody helped his family laugh about the camp's food. He stayed strong for his family and made the best of things.

Despite what the government had put his family through, Woody still felt loyal and chose to serve in the U.S. Army. When internees were asked to pledge their allegiance to the United States by taking the Loyalty Oath, many felt conflicted about how to respond to the government that had stolen their freedom. Woody, however, explained that he wanted to fight in the army because he was an American citizen, and "America is at war" (75). This shows that he considered being American an important part of his identity and felt genuine loyalty. When Papa argued with him, Woody revealed another reason to fight: "The more of us go into the army, the sooner the war will be over, the sooner you and Mama will be out of here" (75). Woody was devoted to his family's welfare in addition to his country, so he chose to fight for them in the most literal way possible.

Woody responded to wartime challenges by expressing his positive attitude and sense of humor to comfort his family. He also chose to join the U.S. Army. It would have been understandable for him to respond to the internment by rioting, but the path he chose instead shows how optimistic, loyal, and caring he was. He was a model American citizen. If President Roosevelt had gotten to know individuals like Woody instead of stereotyping all Japanese Americans, perhaps he would not have signed Executive Order 9066.

Name

Date   Class

Handout 33A: EOM Task Planner

Directions: Use this graphic organizer to plan your informative essay.

	Examples from the Text	What These Examples Show about How the War Affected the Subject's Identity
One sentence stating how the war affected one aspect of this individual's identity:	1. 2. 3.	

	Examples from the Text	What These Examples Show about How the War Affected the Subject's Identity
One sentence stating how the war affected another aspect of this individual's identity:	1. 2. 3.	
Overall, did the subject's wartime experience strengthen or weaken his or her sense of self? Why?		

Name _____

Date _____   Class _____

Handout 35A: Informative Essay Checklist

Directions: Use this checklist to evaluate and revise the draft. Mark a "+" to indicate that the writer has met the criterion. Mark a "Δ" to indicate the need for a change.

Informative Essay Checklist	Self +/ Δ	Peer +/ Δ
Reading Comprehension		
▪ I clearly explain how World War II influenced the individual's identity development.		
▪ I show that I understand the individual's background and wartime experience.		
Structure		
▪ I respond to all parts of the prompt.		
▪ I focus on my topic throughout the piece.		
▪ I introduce the topic clearly in my introduction paragraph, giving a preview of the rest of the essay.		
▪ I organize my ideas clearly in body paragraphs.		
▪ My conclusion paragraph supports the focus.		
▪ I use transitions to smoothly and logically connect paragraphs and ideas.		
Development		
▪ I develop the topic with sufficient evidence from text(s).		
▪ My evidence is relevant to the topic.		
▪ I elaborate upon evidence by analyzing it accurately.		
Style		
▪ I use a variety of sentence patterns (simple, compound, compound-complex) to add clarity and interest to my writing.		
▪ I use vocabulary words that are specific and appropriate to the content.		
▪ I write precisely and concisely, without using unnecessary words.		
▪ I write in a formal style that is appropriate for the audience.		
Conventions		
▪ I spell correctly.		
▪ I use appropriate transitions (phrases and clauses) within and among paragraphs to connect ideas.		
▪ I avoid misplaced and dangling modifiers.		
▪ I punctuate correctly, particularly when using certain transitions, phrases, and clauses.		

<u>To Be Completed by the Peer Reviewer</u>

Peer Reviewer Name:

Praise:

Suggestion:

Name _____

Date _____ Class _____

Handout 35B: Editing and Revising for Style and Conventions

Directions: Use this targeted conventions checklist to annotate at least three points in your essay as follows:

- Identify one place you addressed one of the following correctly.

- Identify one place where you made a mistake that should be corrected.

- Identify a place where you didn't do one of the following, but could add it.

Targeted Style and Conventions Checklist

☐ Correct punctuation in beginning transitions.

    ☐ If a comma is needed, insert one using a caret (^).

    ☐ Example: *In the beginning of the movie a huge explosion occurs.*

☐ Appropriate use of transitional word, phrases, and clauses.

    ☐ Identify errors, and offer suggestions for revision.

☐ A variety of sentence types (simple, compound, complex, compound-complex) and sentence beginnings.

    ☐ Add suggestions for creating variety if sentences are too uniform or writing sounds choppy.

☐ Use of precise and concise language.

    ☐ Identify redundancies, and add suggestions for revision.

    ☐ Note wordiness, and offer suggestions for revision.

☐ Appropriate use of vocabulary studied throughout the module.

Name _____

Date _____ Class _____

Volume of Reading Reflection Questions

Americans All, Grade 7, Module 2

Text:

Author:

Topic:

Genre/type of book:

Share your knowledge about people's experiences and the impact of World War II by answering the questions below.

Informational Texts

1 **Wonder**: What story or parts of the text were difficult to understand? What particular vocabulary, historical details, or background knowledge about World War II or life during this era was helpful to know as you read this book?

2 **Organize**: Summarize a central idea of the text and its development, including relevant details about the experience of the Japanese, the Navajos, or others during WWII.

3 **Reveal**: How do the illustrations contribute to the text? If the text does not include illustrations, how might illustrations change the text?

4 **Distill**: What is the most important insight you gained from this text? How does it relate to World War II?

5 **Know**: How does this text's emphasis on or interpretation of information contrast with that of another text on a similar topic?

6 **Vocabulary**: Write and define three important vocabulary words that you learned in this text. Why is each word important to know in discussions of war and/or in other contexts?

Literary Texts

1 **Wonder**: After reading the first few pages of the text, what inferences can you draw? Support the inferences with textual evidence.

2 **Organize**: Write a short, objective summary of the story including the main character(s), setting, conflict, and resolution.

3 **Reveal**: Select a specific word or phrase. How does that word choice impact the text's meaning and tone?

4 **Distill**: What is a theme of this story? How does it develop over the course of the text?

5 **Know**: How does this text further your understanding of individuals' experiences during World War II? Support your response with details from this text and at least one other text.

6 **Vocabulary**: Identify three words that you learned in this text that are key to understanding the experience of an individual or group during the WWII era. Explain each word's connection.

WIT & WISDOM PARENT TIP SHEET

WHAT IS MY SEVENTH-GRADE STUDENT LEARNING IN MODULE 2?

Wit & Wisdom is our English curriculum. It builds knowledge of key topics in history, science, and literature through the study of excellent texts. By reading and responding to stories and nonfiction texts, we will build knowledge of the following topics:

Module 1: Identity in the Middle Ages

Module 2: Americans All

Module 3: Language and Power

Module 4: Fever

In this second module, *Americans All*, students will explore how we react when faced with war. The World War II experiences of Japanese Americans and Native Americans show how the war impacted Americans in different ways. Students ask, *How did World War II affect individuals?*

OUR CLASS WILL READ THESE TEXTS:

Memoir

- *Farewell to Manzanar*, Jeanne Wakatsuki Houston and James D. Houston

Novel

- *Code Talker*, Joseph Bruchac

Biography

- "Benjamin O. Davis, Jr.," Alexis O'Neill

Historical Account

- "Navajo Code Talkers," Harry Gardiner
- "Pearl Harbor and World War II," Brandon Marie Miller and Mark Clemens
- "Relocation Camps," Craig Blohm
- "World War II Internment of Japanese Americans," Alan Taylor

Articles

- Pearl Harbor Headlines

Music

- "A Beautiful Dawn," Radmilla Cody

OUR CLASS WILL EXAMINE THESE WORKS OF ART:

Photography

- *Manzanar from Guard Tower*, Ansel Adams
- *Photograph of Flag Raising on Iwo Jima, 02/23/1945*, Joe Rosenthal
- *Roy Takeno, outside Free Press Office*, Ansel Adams
- *School Children*, Ansel Adams

Poster

- "Americans All"
- "United We Win"

OUR CLASS WILL ASK THESE QUESTIONS:

- What does being Navajo mean to the protagonist of *Code Talker*?
- How does Ned's Navajo identity provide strength during times of challenge?
- What did the Wakatsukis experience during World War II and how did it affect them?
- How did World War II affect individuals?

QUESTIONS TO ASK AT HOME:

As your seventh-grade student reads, ask:

- *What's happening?*
- *What does a closer look at words and illustrations reveal about this text's deeper meaning?*

BOOKS TO READ AT HOME:

- *Eddie's War*, Carol Fisher Saller
- *Weedflower*, Cynthia Kadohata
- *Dear Miss Breed: True Stories of the Japanese American Incarceration During World War II and a Librarian Who Made a Difference*, Joanne Oppenheim
- *Navajo Code Talkers*, Nathan Aaseng
- *Courage Has No Color*, Tanya Lee Stone

- *Freedom Flyers: The Tuskegee Airmen of WWII*, J. Todd Moye
- *Milkweed*, Jerry Spinelli
- *Hana's Suitcase: The Quest to Solve a Holocaust Mystery*, Karen Levine
- *The Boy on the Wooden Box*, Leon Leyson

IDEAS FOR DISCUSSING WORLD WAR II

Watch movies together that depict the experiences of various Americans during World War II, such as *The Diary of Anne Frank*, *Bridge on the River Kwai*, and *The Battle of Midway*. Ask:

- *What do the characters' identities mean to them during this difficult time?*
- *How did the characters' experiences during World War II affect them?*
- *How did World War II affect these individuals?*

CREDITS

Great Minds® has made every effort to obtain permission for the reprinting of all copyrighted material. If any owner of copyrighted material is not acknowledged herein, please contact Great Minds® for proper acknowledgment in all future editions and reprints of this module.

- All material from the *Common Core State Standards for English Language Arts & Literacy in History/Social Studies, Science, and Technical Subjects* © Copyright 2010 National Governors Association Center for Best Practices and Council of Chief State School Officers. All rights reserved.

- All images are used under license from Shutterstock.com unless otherwise noted.

- Handout 1A: "Benjamin O. Davis, Jr.: 'Determined to Succeed'" by Alexis O'Neill from *Tuskegee Airmen*, Cobblestone magazine, February 1997. Text copyright © 1997 by Carus Publishing Company. Reprinted by permission of Cricket Media. All Cricket Media material is copyrighted by Carus Publishing d/b/a Cricket Media, and/or various authors and illustrators. Any commercial use or distribution of material without permission is strictly prohibited. Please visit http://www.cricketmedia.com/info/licensing2 for licensing and http://www.cricketmedia.com for subscriptions

- Lesson 8 and Handout 9A: Pearl Harbor newspaper images © John Frost Newspapers/Alamy Stock Photo

- Handout 8C: "Pearl Harbor and World War II" by Brandon Marie Miller and Mark Clemens from 30 *Greatest American Events*, Cobblestone magazine, May/June 2010. Text copyright © 2010 by Carus Publishing Company. Reprinted by permission of Cricket Media. All Cricket Media material is copyrighted by Carus Publishing d/b/a Cricket Media, and/or various authors and illustrators. Any commercial use or distribution of material without permission is strictly prohibited. Please visit http://www.cricketmedia.com/info/licensing2 for licensing and http://www.cricketmedia.com for subscriptions

- Handout 18A: "Navajo Code Talkers" by Harry Gardiner from *Dine the People of the Navajo Nation*, Cobblestone magazine, July 1989. Text copyright © 1989 by Carus Publishing Company. Reprinted by permission of Cricket Media. All Cricket Media material is copyrighted by Carus Publishing d/b/a Cricket Media, and/or various authors and illustrators. Any commercial use or distribution of material without permission is strictly prohibited. Please visit http://www.cricketmedia.com/info/licensing2 for licensing and http://www.cricketmedia.com for subscriptions

- Lesson 23, p. 307 and Handout 23A: "Relocation Camps" by Craig Blohm from *World War II The Home Front*, Cobblestone magazine, December 1985. Text copyright © 1985 by Carus Publishing Company. Reprinted by permission of Cricket Media. All Cricket Media material is copyrighted by Carus Publishing d/b/a Cricket Media, and/or various authors and illustrators. Any commercial use or distribution of material without permission is strictly prohibited. Please visit http://www.cricketmedia.com/info/licensing2 for licensing and http://www.cricketmedia.com for subscriptions

- For updated credit information, please visit http://witeng.link/credits.

ACKNOWLEDGMENTS

Great Minds® Staff

The following writers, editors, reviewers, and support staff contributed to the development of this curriculum.

Ann Brigham, Lauren Chapalee, Sara Clarke, Emily Climer, Lorraine Griffith, Emily Gula, Sarah Henchey, Trish Huerster, Stephanie Kane-Mainier, Lior Klirs, Liz Manolis, Andrea Minich, Lynne Munson, Marya Myers, Rachel Rooney, Aaron Schifrin, Danielle Shylit, Rachel Stack, Sarah Turnage, Michelle Warner, Amy Wierzbicki, Margaret Wilson, and Sarah Woodard.

Colleagues and Contributors

We are grateful for the many educators, writers, and subject-matter experts who made this program possible.

David Abel, Robin Agurkis, Elizabeth Bailey, Julianne Barto, Amy Benjamin, Andrew Biemiller, Charlotte Boucher, Sheila Byrd-Carmichael, Eric Carey, Jessica Carloni, Janine Cody, Rebecca Cohen, Elaine Collins, Tequila Cornelious, Beverly Davis, Matt Davis, Thomas Easterling, Jeanette Edelstein, Kristy Ellis, Moira Clarkin Evans, Charles Fischer, Marty Gephart, Kath Gibbs, Natalie Goldstein, Christina Gonzalez, Mamie Goodson, Nora Graham, Lindsay Griffith, Brenna Haffner, Joanna Hawkins, Elizabeth Haydel, Steve Hettleman, Cara Hoppe, Ashley Hymel, Carol Jago, Jennifer Johnson, Mason Judy, Gail Kearns, Shelly Knupp, Sarah Kushner, Shannon Last, Suzanne Lauchaire, Diana Leddy, David Liben, Farren Liben, Jennifer Marin, Susannah Maynard, Cathy McGath, Emily McKean, Jane Miller, Rebecca Moore, Cathy Newton, Turi Nilsson, Julie Norris, Galemarie Ola, Michelle Palmieri, Meredith Phillips, Shilpa Raman, Tonya Romayne, Emmet Rosenfeld, Jennifer Ruppel, Mike Russoniello, Deborah Samley, Casey Schultz, Renee Simpson, Rebecca Sklepovich, Amelia Swabb, Kim Taylor, Vicki Taylor, Melissa Thomson, Lindsay Tomlinson, Melissa Vail, Keenan Walsh, Julia Wasson, Lynn Welch, Yvonne Guerrero Welch, Emily Whyte, Lynn Woods, and Rachel Zindler.

Early Adopters

The following early adopters provided invaluable insight and guidance for Wit & Wisdom:

- Bourbonnais School District 53 • Bourbonnais, IL
- Coney Island Prep Middle School • Brooklyn, NY
- Gate City Charter School for the Arts • Merrimack, NH
- Hebrew Academy for Special Children • Brooklyn, NY
- Paris Independent Schools • Paris, KY
- Saydel Community School District • Saydel, IA
- Strive Collegiate Academy • Nashville, TN
- Valiente College Preparatory Charter School • South Gate, CA
- Voyageur Academy • Detroit, MI

Design Direction provided by Alton Creative, Inc.

Project management support, production design, and copyediting services provided by ScribeConcepts.com

Copyediting services provided by Fine Lines Editing

Product management support provided by Sandhill Consulting